Missing Vowels

Complete each word with a short vowel. Then draw a p

b_zz	cl_ff	s_ck
dr_ss	ch_rry	d_ll
sk_ll	n_ck	tr_ck

1

Which Vowel Sound?

Look at the pictures, decide which ones contain a short vowel sound and colour their borders yellow.

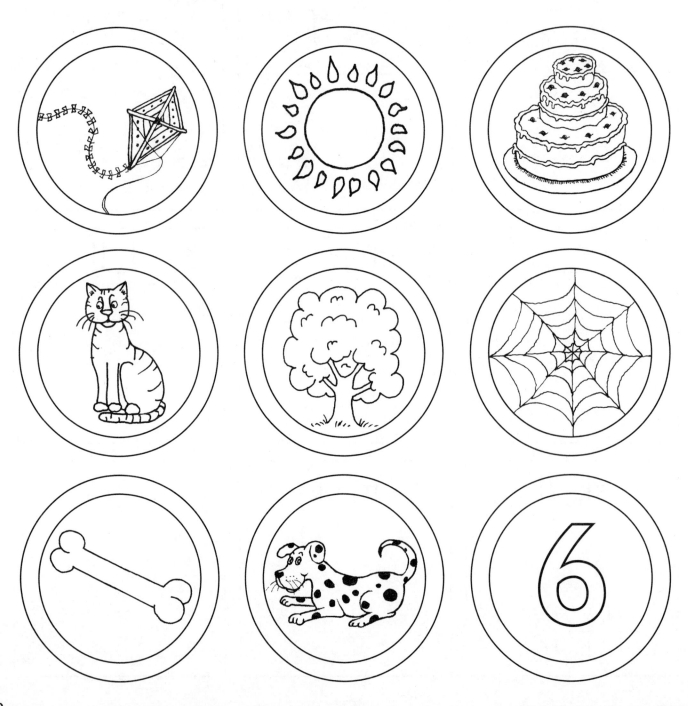

2

Alphabet Colours

Write the alphabet in capital letters, using the four colour groups.

red

yellow

green

blue

What letters come before and after the letters below?

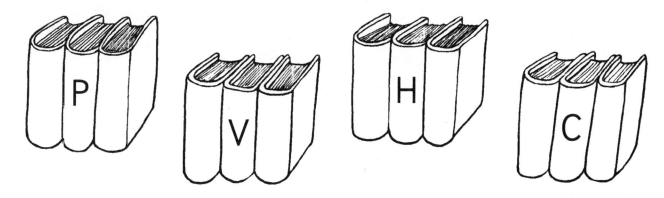

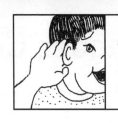

Action: Cup your hand over your ear, as if you are hard of hearing, and say ai, ai, ai?

Add the missing ‹a_e› to each word. Then draw a picture for each one.

4

Proper Nouns

Draw some pictures of your friends and write their names underneath. Remember, a name is a **proper noun** and needs a capital letter.

Inky

Action: Touch your forehead with your index and middle fingers.

Colour: Black

5

Verbs  *Red*

A **verb** is a 'doing' word. Look at the busy bees on the opposite page and write some of the verbs they are doing. Then draw a picture for each one.

to ___fly___   to _____   to _____

to _____   to _____   to _____

to _____   to _____   to _____

Colour the picture and add some bees of your own.

Action: Move your arms backwards and forwards as if you are running.
Colour: Red

Action: Stand to attention, saying *ie, ie!*

like spine

time line

Add the missing ‹i_e› to each word. Then draw a picture for each one.

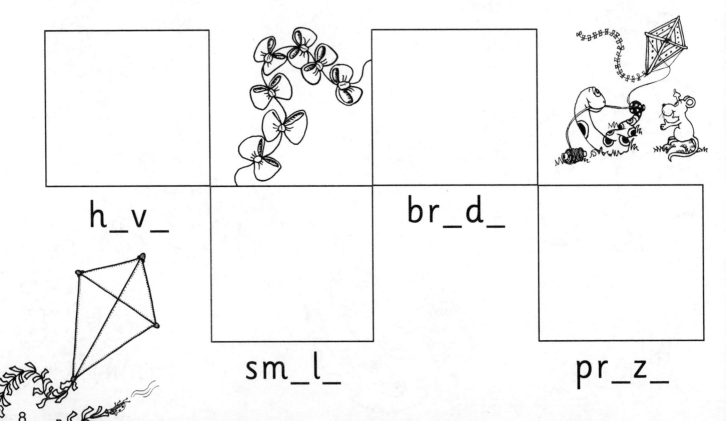

h_v_

sm_l_

br_d_

pr_z_

8

Alphabetical Order

Put the letters into alphabetical order.

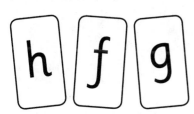 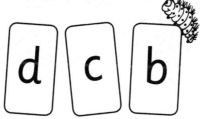 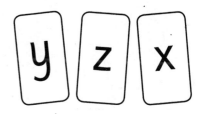

____ ____ ____   ____ ____ ____   ____ ____ ____

____ ____ ____   ____ ____ ____   ____ ____ ____

Use a dictionary to find words beginning with each of the letters below.
Write each word and read its definition.

Aa _____   Dd _____

Ii _____   Mm _____

Pp _____   Ss _____

Xx _____   Zz _____

Verbs  Red

Remind yourself of the pronouns and their actions.

I   you   he she it   we   you   they

Conjugate the verbs in the present tense.

I smile
you smile
he/she/it smiles
we smile
you smile
they smile

to smile

I _____
you _____
he/she/it _____
we _____
you _____
they _____

to tell

I _____
you _____
he/she/it _____
we _____
you _____
they _____

to like

If a verb is happening **now** we use the present tense.

10

Initial Consonant Blends

Match each initial consonant blend to the correct picture.

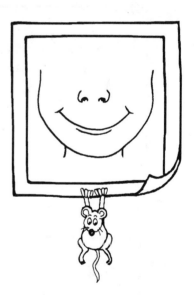

sc- tr- sw- sn- sm- tw-

Action: Bring your hand over your mouth, as if something has gone wrong, and say *oh!*

hope note
tadpole

Add the missing ‹o_e› to each word. Then draw a picture for each one.

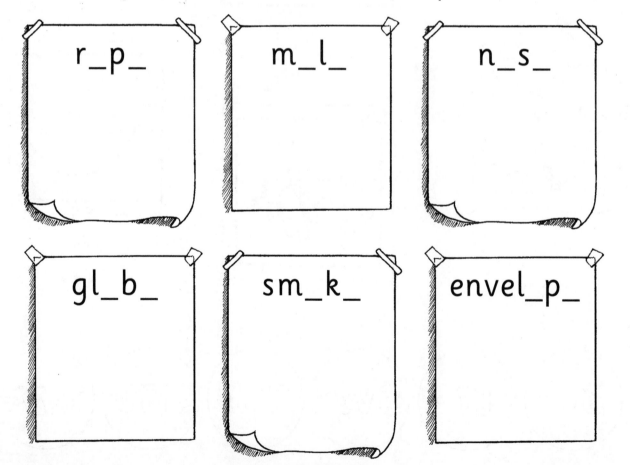

r_p_

m_l_

n_s_

gl_b_

sm_k_

envel_p_

Your Home

Draw a picture of your home and write some sentences about it.

Past Tense Verbs

When we talk about something that has already happened, we use the **past tense**. The simplest way to make the past tense is to put ‹ed› at the end of a verb. If the verb already ends in ‹e›, replace the ‹e› with ‹ed›.

jump + ed = jumped   smil~~e~~ + ed = smiled

wait + ed = waited   wav~~e~~ + ed = waved

Write the following verbs in the past tense.

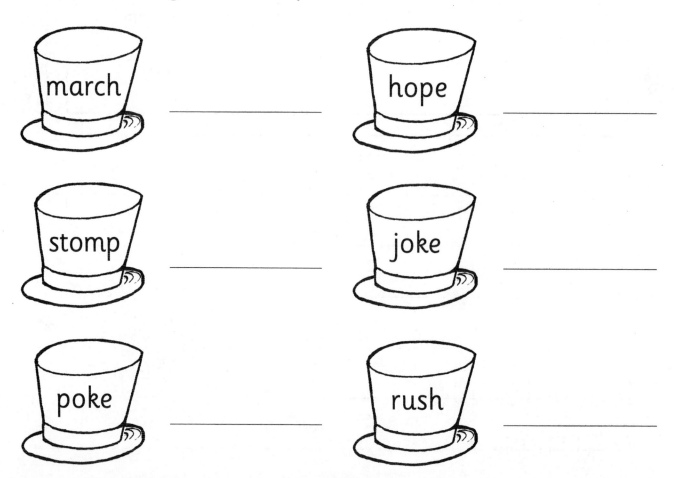

march _____

hope _____

stomp _____

joke _____

poke _____

rush _____

Rewrite the sentences in the past tense.

Today I jump.
Yesterday ___I jumped___.

Today we bake.
Yesterday _____.

Today I cook.
Yesterday _____.

Today they smile.
Yesterday _____.

Today I paint.
Yesterday _____.

Today you play.
Yesterday _____.

u_e

use cube
fuse fumes

Write a sentence using each of the words below.

flute _____

used _____

mule _____

June _____

perfume _____

16

Read and Draw

Magic ‹e› changes a short vowel sound to a long one.

cap   cape

pin   pine

plan   plane

man   mane

spin   spine

rob   robe

Short Vowel Sounds

Sort the words into the correct short vowel containers.

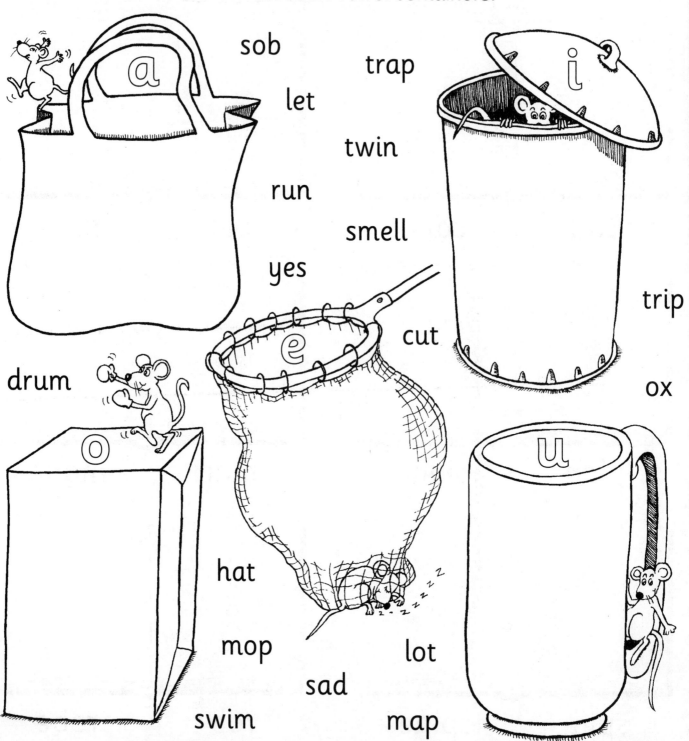

sob

trap

let

twin

run

smell

yes

cut

trip

drum

ox

hat

mop

lot

sad

swim

map

Past Tense Verbs

If a verb ends in a short vowel sound followed by a consonant, the consonant must be doubled before adding ‹ed›. This stops magic ‹e› from changing the short vowel sound into a long one.

dip + p + ed = dipped   bat + t + ed = batted

Write the verbs in the past tense.

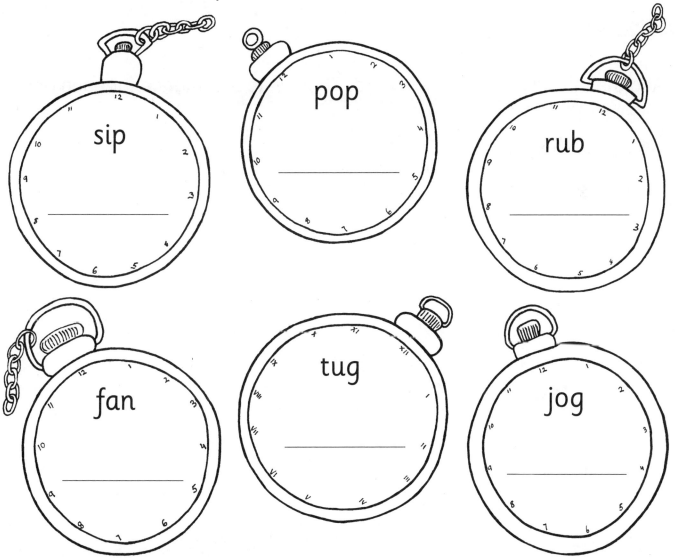

sip _____

pop _____

rub _____

fan _____

tug _____

jog _____

Action: Blow onto your open hand, as if you are the wind, and say *wh, wh, wh*.

Add the missing ‹wh› to each word. Then write a sentence for each one.

_____isk _____

_____ale _____

_____eel _____

_____ite _____

_____iskers _____

Past Tense Verbs

Using a red pencil, colour the flag sections that contain a past tense verb.

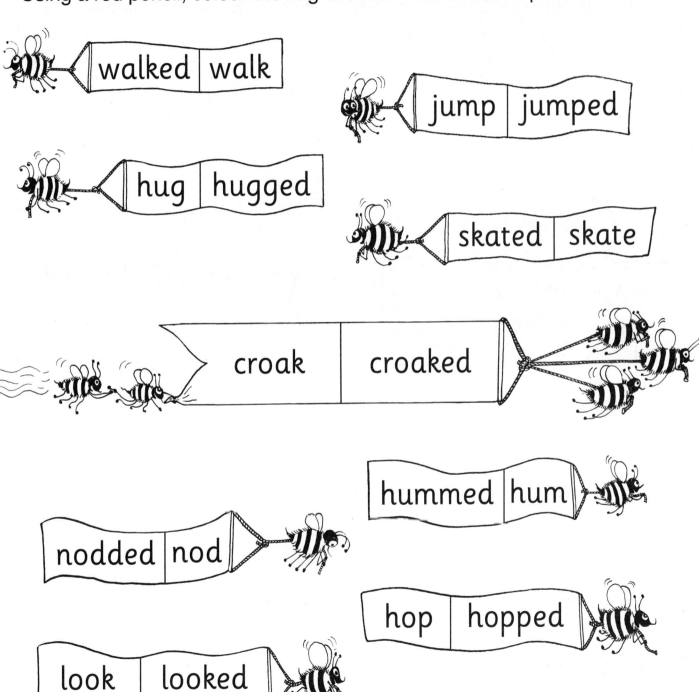

walked | walk

jump | jumped

hug | hugged

skated | skate

croak | croaked

hummed | hum

nodded | nod

hop | hopped

look | looked

Verbs in the future *Red*

> Verbs can describe actions that take place in the future. To show this, an extra verb ('shall' or 'will') is added.

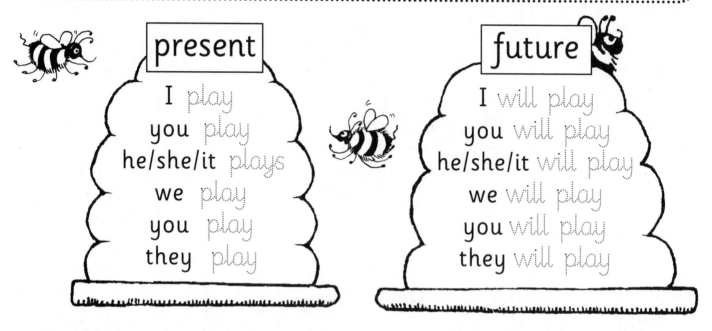

present

I play
you play
he/she/it plays
we play
you play
they play

future

I will play
you will play
he/she/it will play
we will play
you will play
they will play

Are these sentences in the present or future? Circle the correct tense.

I play with my friends.   present / future
I will play with my friends.   present / future

He jumps over the wall.   present / future
He will jump over the wall.   present / future

They will draw some shapes.   present / future
They draw some shapes.   present / future

Past, Present and Future

Write the verbs in the past tense and in the future.

 past

 present

future

past	present	future
I played	I play	I will play
you _____	you smile	you ____ ____
he _____	he cooks	he ____ ____
she _____	she jumps	she ____ ____
it _____	it boils	it ____ ____
I _____	I wave	I ____ ____
you _____	you paint	you ____ ____
he _____	he hops	he ____ ____
she _____	she walks	she ____ ____
it _____	it drips	it ____ ____

	**Past** Point your thumb backwards over your shoulder.		**Present** Point to the floor with the palm of the hand.		**Future** Point to the front.

23

Tricky Words

Write over the dotted words in the flowers, then match them to the words in the pot.

one

only

by

give

have

what

little

live

old

when

like

down

like
live   one

little

when   down
old
what   have
by
give   only